A LIFETIME IN TRACTION

An Engineer on the Southern Diesels and Electrics

Arthur Tayler

A LIFETIME IN TRACTION

An Engineer on the Southern Diesels and Electrics

ARTHUR TAYLER

KRB Publications
2 Denewulf Close
BISHOPS WALTHAM
Hants
SO32 1GZ

www.kevinrobertsonbooks.co.uk

ISBN 0954485920

Printed by the Amadeus Press

Front cover: 10203 depicted at Waterloo in April 1954 , just one month after entering service . (Colour Rail / DE629)

Rear cover, top: Fresh from overhaul, 20002 waits outside Eastleigh running shed for a return to the 'juiced' area.
(Tony Molyneaux)

Rear cover, lower: Former LMS diesel-electric, No. 10000 , near Shawford Junction on the down "Royal Wessex", 1954.
(Colour Rail / DE625)

Previous page: The "Brighton Belleî, with unit 3053 leading (3rd Class Brake No. 92, 1st Class Pullman Cars 'Gwen' and 'Mona', 3rd Class Car No. 85 and 3rd Class Brake No. 93), heading south on the 'Quarry Line'. Three 5-car units, numbered 3051-3 (originally 2051-3) and classified 5BEL, the property of the Pullman Car Company, were built in 1932 by Metropolitan Cammell with the same motors and control gear as the 6PUL units. Running and electrical equipment was serviced by the Southern. Note the roof train name boards and mixture of flat bottom and bullhead rail.

Track circuit and AWS interference tests taking place near to Durley Halt on the Bishops Waltham branch in 1959. This short branch had lost its passenger service in 1933, and aside from a single daily freight service, there was no other regular traffic. As such it was an ideal candidate for test purposes. The tests involved a short section of the branch being wired for AWS to gauge the response obtained from the unit - which was, of course, AWS fitted. Results could then be compared with those obtained in other areas where the return current from 3rd rail electrified lines sometimes caused disruption to the indication received from the AWS .

Note

Unless otherwise stated, all the photographs are by the author or from his collection.

INTRODUCTION AND BRIEF BIOGRAPHY

I was a fourth-generation railwayman, but the first to enter the engineering side of the industry. I was born in the second floor back bedroom of my Grandparents' three-storey house in Effingham Road, Surbiton, a road running parallel to the former London and South Western main line between Hampton Court Junction and Surbiton. I was interested in the railway from an early age and two boarding schools, the Prebendal School at Chichester and Ardingly College, Sussex did nothing to diminish it, rather the reverse.

When I expressed interest in 'working on the railway' to a friend of my Grandfather, a Civil Engineer, formerly with the London and South Western and Southern Railways, he advised me to look to the electrical side of the industry, as that was where the future lay.

A letter to the Chief Electrical Engineer of the Southern Railway, R. Alfred Raworth, then in his sixty-second year, resulted in an interview in February 1942 with A. E. Moore, Assistant Electrical Engineer at Deepdene House in Dorking, Surrey. I was sent some drawings to transpose into a different scale, and being in the sixth form, the second term of the first year, I was able to do the drawings in class.

My drawings were accepted, and I was offered a job as a Temporary Junior Draughtsman at £1.17s.6d (£1.88) per week - only temporary posts were available in wartime to cover vacancies left by staff who were in the Armed Services. On 1st June 1942, two days after my 17th birthday I reported to the Chief Draughtsman, W. J. Webb, at Deepdene House. Registration for conscription was then at 18 years of age so I would have one year at most until I was liable for 'call-up'.

My first task was to update some substation drawings. The leading draughtsman, Harry Marchant, soon discovered I had a good knowledge of rolling stock, so he put me on to up-dating the rolling stock diagram books, which were used widely in the department and elsewhere. My knowledge of rolling stock stood me in good stead, and these 1/8in to 1ft drawings posed no problem, so from that time, my work was concentrated on rolling stock.

In September 1942, I enrolled for weekend classes for the BSc Intermediate course in Electrical Engineering at Northampton Polytechnic, Islington, and when I received call-up papers at 18, was advised to apply for deferment. I was then called before a Selection Board, who granted me deferment from call-up, provided I put in the required attendance and passed the relevant exams. Either ARP (Air Raid Precaution) duty or Home Guard was compulsory (I opted for the latter), and this left little or no time for socialising. I did manage to keep up, and even add to my "O" gauge model railway, as and when money and materials were available, mostly from second hand sources.

During the next two years I worked on a variety of jobs, all on rolling stock, such as fitting additional heaters in the driving cabs of the former LSWR motor coaches; strengthening the operating lever of the Waterloo & City trip cocks; designing a new pneumatically-operated ice scraper, and applying this to the shoe beams of the first Co-Co-electric locomotive CC1, as well as electric multiple units, and many other small jobs.

I sat the Intermediate examinations in June 1944, at the Imperial Institute in South Kensington, London, at the height of the V1 and V2 bombardment. At this time Alfred Raworth was preparing for retirement, and in early 1945 his post was filled by Charles M. Cock, an Australian who had come to the Southern Railway via India, where he had been Electrical Engineer on the Great Indian Peninsular Railway - a system electrified at 1500 Volts dc.

The War in Europe ended in May 1945, and the Department prepared for the move back to London, which came in September 1945 when we moved to 15 St Thomas Street, London SE1. This was formerly the property of the South Eastern Railway, who acquired it in a deal with St Thomas' Hospital in 1862, when the hospital moved to its present location close to Westminster Bridge. The offices were relatively small and inconveniently placed, and heating was by coal fires! We were on the second floor, which was accessed by stairs with lead-covered treads.

At the same time, I was promoted to the post of Temporary Junior Technical Assistant, one of two assistants to W J Arnold Sykes, then Rolling Stock New Works Engineer. I had been working with Arnold Sykes on a temporary basis for nearly a year before the move, so when the second electric locomotive was commissioned, I was given the job of test engineer on trial runs between Brighton and London Victoria. The heat for call-up was off, but I was still liable for two years National Service following completion of my studies.

In 1946, I was offered an exchange with a junior engineer of the erstwhile English Electric Company. This involved a one-year student apprenticeship in their workshops, commencing on 1st November 1946. My opposite number was the late W. McCraith, who later became a Director of Lawrence Scott of Norwich.

Opposite page:
The second Co-Co electric locomotive, 20002 (formerly CC2). *Stored during World War II, the second locomotive was equipped at Brighton in 1945, and I was sent as an observer on the trial trips, which were carried out on the Brighton main line. Here, as BR 20002, it is outside Peckham Rye repair shops waiting for a traction motor change. Note the multiple-unit control receptacles and twin-air brake pipes. Otherwise externally it was similar to 20001. Electrically, there were minor changes, and this was the first locomotive to be provided with dual controls for one-man operation, although it was to be many years before one-man operation was actually achieved. The dullness of the 'silver' roof and bogie frames shows how impractical was the livery.*

A Lifetime in Traction

The course involved spells at four English Electric factories producing traction equipment - six months in Bradford, equally divided between traction control gear and motors, one month in Stafford on transformers and rectifiers, three months on diesel engines at Preston, a further month at Rugby, and a final month in Derby, nominally on locomotive erection and testing. In fact, much of this last month was spent working on the main wiring diagram of the first two main-line diesel-electric locomotives; 10000 was then in the final stages of erection in Derby Locomotive Works.

While in Bradford, in March 1947, I was established on the permanent staff as a Junior Technical Assistant. Two former members of the department had failed to return from the services, which left two vacancies. There was a small increase in salary, which covered the contribution I was now obliged to make to the pension fund, plus a small bit over! My weekly salary by then, with annual increments of 5s and a merit increase, had reached the princely sum of £4.10s.0d (£4.50), or £235 per annum before deductions. My 'digs' took £2.2s.0d (£2.10)! During the six months in Bradford, I completed my studies at Bradford Technical College.

I returned to the Southern Railway at the beginning of November 1947, two months prior to Nationalisation, and after a short spell on electric multiple unit inspection and testing, was transferred in the autumn of 1948 to the locomotive section to work on the first order for 15 diesel-electric shunting locomotives. The five months of my Student Apprenticeship spent working with diesel engines and locomotives put me in an almost unique position. Additionally, the third electric locomotive was being erected at Eastleigh, and I spent time there as well.

Project management on electric and diesel-electric locomotives and multiple-units was my speciality for the next fifteen years. The expected conscription for National Service was still hanging over me, but never materialised. Some years later I discovered the Railway had managed to block it when I was put on to the permanent staff.

On 1st January 1948, the railways were nationalised and C. M. Cock was appointed Chief Officer for Electrical Engineering of the new Railway Executive, and was succeeded by Stanley B. Warder, formerly the Region's Power Supply Engineer. In September 1949, on Bulleid's retirement, Warder became acting Chief Mechanical & Electrical Engineer. He was assisted for a time by R. A. Smeddle from the North Eastern Region as his deputy. Warder succeeded Cock as Chief Electrical Engineer of British Railways when Cock joined the erstwhile English Electric Company in 1952. Smeddle was appointed CM&EE of the Western Region, and H. H. Swift from the Eastern Region was appointed CM&EE of the Southern Region for the next four years, when he too retired. He was in turn succeeded by W. J. Arnold Sykes, who had joined the Southern Railway in 1930 after an apprenticeship with the then District Railway at Acton Works. I worked with Arnold Sykes

from 1944. He was a man with considerable knowledge and experience of electric traction, with whom I had a good rapport, and he taught me a great deal. I enjoyed working under him for close on fifteen years.

I was elected first a Graduate, then Associate Member of the erstwhile Institution of Locomotive Engineers and attended most of the London meetings on subjects of great railway interest. This gave me an introduction to many eminent railway engineers, and was to be a help in later years. When in October 1969 the ILocoE was merged with the IMechE, and became its Railway Division, I was elected a Member of the Institution of Mechanical Engineers, and obtained Chartered Engineer status. Later, I became the Chairman of the Railway Division Visits Committee, a member of the Division Board and was elected a Fellow of the Institution.

In 1954, I was appointed Assistant for Locomotives and Diesel-Electric Multiple-Units (New Works). My responsibilities had previously included the project work for the 26 diesel-electric shunting locomotives, the two 1750 hp and the 2000 hp main-line diesel-electric locomotives. Now there were the 75 diesel-electric multiple units, the 24 2,552 hp Bo-Bo electric locomotives for the Kent Coast electrification (later class 71), the 98 Type 3 (class 33) 1,550 hp diesel-electric locomotives and the six prototype 1,600 hp electro-diesels (later class 73/0). I also played a large part in the decision to build 43 more electro-diesels for the Bournemouth electrification. In addition, it was my duty to oversee modifications to the traction equipment of these and other diesel and electric locomotives operating on the Region.

In the early part of 1964, I was offered and accepted the post of Head of the Erection and Service Department in the Traction Division of Sulzer Bros (London) Limited, as they then were. The manager, and by then Special Director of the Traction Division, was Tom Schur, who had head-hunted me with the ultimate aim of succeeding him in London when he later moved to Switzerland. I commenced work in the London offices on 28th March, and to gain experience of the Sulzer Traction Design, Development and Manufacturing organisation, I was sent in April, first to Winterthur in Switzerland for a month, then to France for two weeks, based in the Paris offices of the French Sulzer company, Compagnie Constructions MÈcanique Procédés Sulzer, or CCM as they were usually known.

The CCM works were at Mantes, some 33 miles to the west of Paris, where the 12LVA24 engines were being manufactured and tested. Visits were also made to SNCF depots at Chalindrey and Caen, and the workshops at Épernay and Sotteville (Rouen) to observe maintenance and repair procedures on the same engines. At that time there were fourteen in service in 68000 class A1A-A1A locomotives, as well as two 8LVA24 engines in Bo-Bo locomotives based in Besançon. Five 12LVA24 engines and one 16LVA24 engine were later to work on British Railways.

On returning to London, I took full charge of the Traction

A Hampton Court to Waterloo train leaving Surbiton. Lengthened 4SUB unit 4411 forms an up Sunday morning stopping train calling at all stations to Waterloo in the summer of 1953. Unit 4411 was originally a 3-car unit of the 1928 era of converted LSWR stock. By this time, it had been lengthened to 4 cars by the insertion of a 10 compartment all-steel trailer, one of a batch of 163 built for the purpose. The bridge in the background carries the A240 Ewell Road.

Erection and Service Department, and in 1966, was appointed Manager of the Traction Division in London. Later, in January 1976 when the Company, by then Sulzer (UK) Ltd., moved to Farnborough, Hants, I took charge of the combined Traction and Marine Service and Spares departments with the title of Manager - Diesel Department, Farnborough.

By 1966, the European market was saturated with diesel locomotives, and Sulzer concluded they could no longer afford to design and build engines alone for a single specialist market. After a period of development work on the uprated LVA24 engines in collaboration with the former English Electric Company, who at the time took a Sulzer license, it was hoped, vainly as it happened, that the latter would build and sell the Sulzer LVA24 range of engines. Sulzer finally wound up their Traction Department in Winterthur in 1977 to concentrate on the Marine and Stationary markets.

The UK spares and components business remained buoyant for another twenty years with technical backing from the Swiss Diesel department. However rationalisation of locomotive types by British Railways reduced the demand for spares, and in the late 1970s I had the task of trying to interest British Railways in the Sulzer ASV25/30 engine as a possible alternative to Ruston for the class 56 and 58 locomotives. The ASV25/30 engine had been developed alongside the LVA24 for the larger Marine and Stationary market, and bore remarkable similarities in design, but nothing was actually interchangeable! With the demise of traction and the LVA24, the ASV25/30 had a possible traction application both in the UK and abroad. Support from Switzerland was rather half-hearted, as they had aspirations on the North American market, and were seeking a US license, later taken up by Waukesha (Dresser Industries).

To obtain experience under North American conditions,

four 12ASV25/30 engines set to 3,200hp (2,800 hp for traction) were installed in Morrison-Knudsen rebuilds of Southern Pacific GE U25B Bo-Bo locomotives; ten 4,300hp (4,000 hp for traction) 16ASV25/30 engines were installed in rebuilds of EMD SD45 Co-Co locomotives, four for Union Pacific and six for Burlington Northern. Morrison-Knudsen also built a 1500 hp 'Demonstrator' - a Bo-Bo converted from an Alco RS3 with a 6ASL25/30 in-line engine, and this visited a number of yards in the USA.

In May 1980, I visited the USA in company with two senior engineers, Mike Whattam and Larry Shore, from British Railways, who were impressed with the 12ASV25/30 engines operating on Southern Pacific. However by 1982 Sulzer had lost interest in further development for traction of the ASL25/30 engine, and the potential British Railways business, at best small, was dropped, those engines in the USA locomotives going the way of other European prototypes - they had a short life and were abandoned.

By the beginning of 1983, there was insufficient work with Sulzer to keep me fully employed, and there were no other suitable opportunities with the Company. Fortunately in March of that year the post of Executive Officer of the IMechE Railway Division became vacant at IMechE headquarters. I joined the staff, and later became Manager of the Railway Division which post I held for another seven years until retirement on my sixty-fifth birthday at the end of May 1990.

Now follow photographs with brief descriptions of various types of locomotives and multiple units with which I was involved in one way or another over forty-one years; five-and-a-half years with the Southern Railway, almost sixteen-and-a-half years with the Southern Region of British Railways and nineteen years with Sulzer, during which time I was elected a Fellow of the Institution of Mechanical Engineers and served on the Divisional Board as Chairman of the Visits Committee. The seven years with the Institution of Mechanical Engineers were a bonus, as I still had contact with many of my former colleagues of both British Railways and the railway supply industry, so was able to keep up with developments.

I have selected just over a hundred photographs, from my collection. The pictures are, in the main, my own and I apologise if the quality of some of them is not up to standard. They do however represent periods in my career which were significant, and I ask the reader's indulgence!

Eastbourne and Hastings (1935) 6-car unit with pantry car (6PAN)
A Victoria-Ore evening service with 6PAN 3034 (originally 2034) and a 6PUL unit passes Norman's Bay Halt in August 1964, greeted by my two children, then eight and five years of age. The motor coaches were divided between Metropolitan Cammell and BRCW, with the same control gear as for the 6PUL units. The traction motors, identical to those on the 6PUL, units were made by the English Electric Company. Note the short (59ft 0in) Trailer First ahead of the "Pantry" car, the "Air Stream" ventilators and flat-bottom rail on the up line. The headcode indicates that the train took the direct leg of the erstwhile Polgate/Pevensey triangle.

1932/3 Southern Railway 6-car express unit with Pullman car (6PUL)

6PUL unit 3012 with Pullman Car "Bertha" is leaving Quarry Tunnel on Sunday 13th April 1958, forming the 10.25 Victoria to Littlehampton via Hove. 20 units, numbered 3001-20 (originally 2001-20), were built in 1932; the Motor and Pullman cars by Metropolitan Cammell and the other trailer cars by the Southern Railway for fast services to Brighton and West Worthing.. The motor coaches had four 225hp (1-hour) MV 163 traction motors (made by BT-H) and low-voltage electro-pneumatic control gear by Metro-Vick. Units were run singly or in pairs. Note the 1932 3-aspect colour light signal, flat bottom rail on the down line, the destination board just behind the Guard's Van doors, BR emblem on the motor coach side and overhead telephone wires. e motor coaches had four)MV 163 traction motors (made by BT-H) and low voltage electro-pneumatic control gear by Metro-Vick. Units were run singly or in pairs. Note the 1932 3-aspect colour light signal; FB rail on the down line; the destination board just behind the Guard's Van doors; BR emblem on the motor coach side; overhead telephone wires.

An empty stock working from Wimbledon to Woking
An empty train of four two-car units led by No. 2120 is entering Surbiton on the down through line composed of four units; two 2BIL sets, one 2NOL, and a final 2BIL. The time was about 1645 and the stock was probably for an up train between Woking and Waterloo, which later still would form the one evening train from Waterloo to Ascot, traversing the slow line from Pirbright Junction and Sturt Lane Junction.

Opposite page:

Semi-Fast Stock for the Portsmouth, Alton and Reading services - 1937-9
Thirty-three four-car units (4LAV) were built in 1932 for the semi-fast services of the Brighton electrification, but subsequent schemes had 2-car units. Designated 2BIL with one motor and one driving trailer car, each with a side corridor to a lavatory at the inner end, 152 were built. The first ten, originally numbered 1891-1900, built in 1935 (re-numbered 2001-2010 in 1937), had Metropolitan Vickers cab-mounted electromagnetic control gear. The rest, built in three batches between 1937 and 1939, were numbered 2011-2152, and had English Electric electro-pneumatic undercar control gear. All had English Electric manufactured type 339 traction motors of 275hp (1-hour). Here a Sunday Waterloo to Alton and Portsmouth & Southsea stopping train passes the junction with the Sutton line in June 1954 led by 2060, one of the second batch built for the Mid-Sussex electrification in 1938. Note the flat bottom rails on all four running lines and the 1937 (Westinghouse) semi-automatic colour light signals.

Portsmouth Electrification "Express" 4-car units Type 4COR/4RES

The 16.20 Waterloo-Portsmouth Harbour train near West Weybridge (later Byfleet and New Haw) on a Saturday in July 1953. 4-car units had more flexibility, and so that the catering car could be accessible from all seats, end gangways were provided which gave the 'one-eye' appearance; hence the stock was dubbed 'Nelsons'. The normal train formation was 4COR/4RES/4COR on the Portsmouth 'direct' line and 4COR/4BUF/4COR on the Mid-Sussex line. Originally, 55 4CORs, 19 4RES and 13 4BUF units were built, the latter for the 1938 Mid-Sussex electrification. War damage, and changed requirements, resulted in the numbers being revised to 58, 14 and 13 respectively. Motor coaches had two EE163 traction motors and undercar electro-pneumatic control gear. Unit 3142 has been preserved and is being brought up to running standard.

2BIL units on South Coast stopping service.
Approaching Norman's Bay Halt for Hastings in August 1964, unit 2118 is one of the third batch built in 1938 for the Staines-Ascot-Reading and Aldershot-Guildford electrification. Although built for specific schemes, they were used in pool and could be seen anywhere between Hastings and Portsmouth. This batch had strengthened underframes and "self-contained" buffers with heavy castings. First used in 1932 on "express" stock, these buffers were used on the outer ends of all new stock from 1938 until 1951.

Preserved 2BIL and 4SUB Units
Preserved 2BIL 2090, built in 1938 for the Mid-Sussex electrification, is at the 'Basingstoke 150' weekend on Sunday 26th September 1987. 2090, with preserved 4SUB 4732 (class 405), worked a shuttle service between Basingstoke and Woking. Seen in the down slow platform at Basingstoke, 4732, although of Southern Railway design, was built at Eastleigh in 1950 in BR days and was similar to the 4SUB units I inspected, tested and passed for traffic! Note that the 2BIL still carries the "stencil" route indicator numerals; twin air horns have replaced the old compressed air whistle, while the full yellow ends and black "triangle" indicate the vehicle with the luggage van. Spring-loaded lightweight shoegear has replaced the original heavy gravity type.

Stock for the 1938 Gillingham and Maidstone Electrification (2HAL)

The 2HAL units comprised a compartment motor third coupled to a side corridor composite lavatory driving trailer to give more seats than the 2BILs. Oliver Bulleid became CME in 1937, and this stock reflects changes brought about in the early days of his regime, some detrimental to passenger comfort! I was horrified to find, when travelling on a 2HAL for the first time, how hard was the bench-type seating compared to the cushions on the 2BILs. Electrically identical to the 2BILs, seventy-six units were built for the Gillingham and Maidstone lines and a further sixteen as 'Additional Rolling Stock' for general use in 1939. A Saturday Waterloo-Sandown Park-Woking race special passes Weybridge in April 1963 with 3 x 2HAL units led by 2670, one of the first batch.

The Southern Railway's first mixed-traffic electric locomotive No CC1
The Southern had a proportionately smaller volume of freight traffic than the other three companies, and it was handled by steam locomotives. Alfred Raworth had the view that freight and "through" passenger traffic should be handled by electric locomotives. Two Co-Co 1470hp mixed traffic locomotives were authorised by the Southern Railway in 1938, and were put in hand at Ashford Works. Although two sets of mechanical parts were built, War conditions allowed completion of only one, numbered CC1, and the first trial run was in January 1941 between Brighton and Three Bridges. Two of my school friends and I were at Copyhold Junction that morning, and were surprised and thrilled to see this new machine. We cycled to Three Bridges that afternoon and were rewarded to see CC1 at close hand when it reversed on the up slow line platform. This locomotive leaves Victoria on a dull afternoon in 1951 with a Pullman special to Eastbourne, renumbered 20001, and painted in the livery for 'non-steam' locomotives - black with a silver waist strip, roof and bogies. Originally equipped with a multiple unit 'stencil-type' route indicator, the six electric marker lights were added in 1944.

Opposite page, lower: **Double-deck unit 4001 at London Bridge**
This was on the occasion of a special run for the Lord President of the Council, Herbert Morrison, and 4001 is entering platform 10 at London Bridge. At this time, November 1949, the unit had the original bolsterless bogies, with fabricated wheels of 3ft 2in diameter. After a few days in traffic, cracks were found in the wheels, and 4001/2 had to be withdrawn from service for some weeks until normal-type bogies with standard wheelsets could be fitted. Both units ran some 700,000 miles in service before being replaced by 10-coach trains.

Lengthened "Guildford & Dorking" 3-car unit 1304 as 4SUB 4310
Electrification reached Guildford via Cobham, and Dorking via Epsom, in 1926. 26 3-car units, numbered 1285-1310, were built in 1925 by contractors; Metropolitan Carriage, Wagon & Finance Company the motor coaches, and Midland Railway Carriage and Wagon Company the trailers. Electrical equipment by Metropolitan Vickers was similar to the 1915 LSWR stock. In 1939, the SR decided to standardize on 4-car units and 55 steel-bodied trailers were built in 1945/6. 26 of these were used to "lengthen" these 3-car units. Note the LSWR front-end shape and the 8ft 6in wide practically straight-sided bodies; the 10 compartment additional trailer has a curved profile, 9ft 0in wide body and a wood and canvas roof. 4310 enters Clapham Junction on a Hampton Court service on a Saturday in June 1952.

Opposite page: ***20002 in British Railways "Electric" green.***
Following BR's foray into employing "Industrial Designers", various livery changes were made. All Southern Region electric locomotives and multiple units were painted in BR "Electric" green - a darker shade than the Bulleid "Malachite" - and this was applied to 20001-3 after the black and silver period. 20002 is outside Stewarts Lane depot in 1960, having been hauled from Eastleigh after overhaul. The roof and underframe channels are a light grey, and there is a red stripe, edged by white, along the centre of the bodysides between the cab doors. By this time the Multiple Unit equipment had been removed on my authorisation.

Left: **Preserved 4SUB (class 405) 4732 with preserved 2BIL 2090**
These two units are entering Southampton on 10th May 1985 for a special to Eastleigh and Winchester for members and guests of the Railway Division of the Institution of Mechanical Engineers. Although 4732 is painted in the style adopted by the former Southern Railway prior to Nationalisation, it was not built until 1951, and never carried "Southern" above the windows. Changes include the twin air horns on the cab roof, the later type of air-operated windscreen wiper and lightweight collector shoes.

*Above: **All-steel 4SUB (class 405) 4673 of 1950 build***
A Victoria-Orpington working is seen on the 1902 down spur from the old LC&DR main line to the former SER main line near Petts Wood Junction on 16th February 1955. The spurs were realigned in 1960/1, and the former LC&DR main line quadrupled to Swanley. Further alterations were made in 1996/7 to cater for Eurostar. Note the air intakes for traction motor ventilation on the Guard's van roof, bullhead rails throughout, with more of the same waiting as replacements and stencil-type route indicator

*Opposite page, top: **Post-War all-steel 4SUB (class 405) 4630***
Passing Factory Junction on the up 'fast' line, with an Orpington-Victoria service in June 1961, 4630 was one of 32 new units built at Eastleigh in 1949 with self-ventilated lightweight EE 507C traction motors. This was one of the units that I inspected at Eastleigh, and tested at Selhurst. Wandsworth Road station (behind) is on the South London line, which curves away in the background to join the Brighton main line at Battersea Park. The tracks leading to Stewarts Lane depot and Latchmere Junction can also be seen. Note the heavy 150 lb/yd conductor rails on all three main line tracks and the bullhead running rails. Today this piece of line is traversed by Eurostars.

First electrically-hauled Newhaven boat train
15th April 1949 saw the Newhaven Boat Trains handed over to electric locomotive haulage, initially working to 'steam' timings. From the 'summer' timetables of July, new schedules nine minutes shorter were substituted. 20003, in BR black and silver livery, prepares to leave Victoria with the 09.05 day Newhaven Continental. Steam for train heating was provided from an electrically-heated boiler, and would continue for another 15 years. Note the carmine and cream livery of the locomotive-hauled coaching stock.

Opposite page, top: **The third Co-Co electric locomotive No 20003**
This locomotive was authorised by the former Southern Railway to replace T14 class 4-6-0 No 458, which was destroyed by a bomb on Nine Elms in 1940. CC3 was 1ft 6in longer than the first two, to provide more roomy driving cabs and an extra 6in for the equipment compartments; the exterior was restyled to match the current electric multiple-unit stock. Traction equipment had increased electrical capacity, with an updated type EE519 traction motor and the control gear was modified to simplify driving. Control sockets and air pipes were provided for multiple operation. Numbered 20003 by BR, and intended to be the prototype for the future, the plans allowed for two locomotives in multiple on certain trains. I spent some time in the works at Eastleigh during the later stages of erection, then organised the early trial running on the Brighton line. 20003 was completed at Eastleigh in September 1948, and is seen here in malachite green with yellow lining; it was repainted early in 1949 in black. 20003 is seen here about to depart from Norwood Yard with a heavy goods. Opposite page, lower: UR TAYLER

Opposite page, lower: **Exhibition of Modern British Railways Locomotives**
In July 1952, an exhibition of "modern" BR locomotives was held at Eastbourne for delegates to a UIC Convention. Here 20003 is being shunted into position by former LBSCR E5 class 0-6-2T No. 32405, itself withdrawn from service in November of 1952. Other motive power on exhibition included the latest examples of BR 'Standard' steam locomotives of class 7 4-6-2, class 5 4-6-0 and class 4 4-6-0, together with the "Fell" 2,000 hp diesel-mechanical locomotive and one of the Southern 350hp diesel-electric shunters.

The "Fell" diesel-mechanical locomotive 10100

The "Fell" 2000hp diesel-mechanical locomotive, No 10100, with the first of the second batch of Southern diesel-electric shunters, 15227. 10100, the brain-child of Lt Col L F R Fell of Rolls Royce, had four Paxman 12RPHXL 500hp engines driving through fluid couplings and differentials into a central gearbox. There were also two AEC 150hp auxiliary engines driving positive displacement blowers, and providing auxiliary power. Purchased by BR in May 1955, it did not live up to its designer's expectations, and was withdrawn in February 1960 after a disastrous fire in the erstwhile Manchester Central station.

Opposite page, top: Southern Railway 350 hp diesel-electric shunting locomotive 15215

Just prior to Nationalisation, the Southern Railway ordered fifteen 350hp diesel-electric shunters, part authorised in 1939, but held in abeyance until the end of the Second World War, and later increased to 26. The power equipment was similar to that in the locomotives designed and built by the LMS, and Derby drawings were used for the mechanical parts, modified where necessary, principally to accommodate 4ft 6in diameter wheels. Gearing for a top speed of 27 mph (maximum tractive effort 24,000 lb) allowed transfer over main lines from depots at Norwood Junction and Hither Green to various yards where they were used for flat shunting. 15215 is seen here as the Ashford Works pilot in June 1950. The management of this build was my first diesel job, after returning from my year with English Electric.

Opposite page, lower: Experimental diesel-mechanical 0-6-0 shunter

Intended to be able to work on yard shunting as well as pick-up goods duties, this 500 hp locomotive was completed at Ashford in 1950, and photographed at that time. It had a Paxman 12RHP engine coupled to a two-range, three-speed gearbox through a Sinclair fluid coupling. In the high-speed range, it was originally intended to be able to run at a maximum speed of 45 mph. It turned out to be neither one thing nor the other. The low-speed range was too inflexible for shunting, and the high-speed range, with only three gear steps, was too low for line duties. It worked from Norwood for a time, spent a long time out of service, and was finally discarded in 1959.

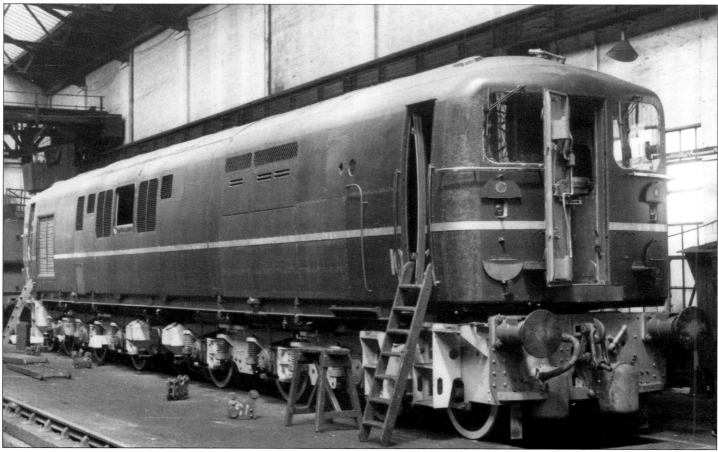

An Engineer on the Southern Diesels and Electrics

Southern main line diesel-electric locomotive 10202
10202 was completed in August 1951, by which time BR Headquarters had ordered a change of gear ratio. New gears had an 18-month lead time so BR decided 10201/2 should remain on their parent Region. On 15th October 1951, 10202 began work on the West of England main line where, despite its high-speed gear ratio, it was usefully employed on a 4-leg diagram between Waterloo and Exeter covering 687 revenue-earning miles each day. Here 10202 is passing Surbiton in December 1951, on the 07.30 from Exeter. I would often ride on the locomotive with the 01.25 to Exeter and the 07.30 return on the Monday after maintenance.

Opposite page, top: **The first Southern diesel-electric main line locomotive 10201**
Soon after the LMS announced they were to build two 1600hp main line diesel-electric locomotives, the Southern announced an order for three 1600hp locomotives for a high-speed service between Waterloo and Plymouth. West of Exeter, the maximum axle load was limited to 18.5 tons hence the 1Co-Co1 wheel arrangement. Geared for a top speed of 110 mph, 10201 was completed in December 1950, and this photograph was taken in the erecting shop at Ashford in August 1950, with the English Electric 16SVT engine in place. By the time 10201 was built, the engine had been uprated to 1750 hp. After testing and about four weeks in service between Derby and St Pancras, 10201 was exhibited at the 'Festival of Britain' until the early winter of 1951

Opposite page, lower: **1750hp 1-Co-Co-1 locomotive 10201 almost complete in Ashford Works**
This is a shot taken in the erecting shop at Ashford in the autumn of 1950, just after the body had been lowered on to the bogies, which had already been painted in aluminium paint. 10201 was tested and ran trials between Ashford and Ramsgate in early December 1950 before final painting. The door in the cab front was intended to give access to a second locomotive coupled in multiple unit.

The first new design suburban 4-car unit 5001
With 44 years of service ahead of it, 5001, the first 4EPB (class 415) stands at Wimbledon Park in April 1951. The 4EPBs embodied the first major change of power and brake equipment for suburban and semi-fast stock, although the coach design followed previous Southern practice. Four EE507D traction motors of 250hp (1-hour) gave an acceleration rate of 1.25 mph/sec to 27 mph with a maximum speed of 75 mph. Lightweight control gear was used, with low voltage lighting from a 73-volt motor-generator and battery. Self-lapping electro-pneumatic brakes were fitted. Visible mechanical changes at the front end are buckeye automatic couplers and driver's cab with sliding windows. Controls were grouped in a desk and entry to the cab was from the Guard's compartment with control jumpers and duplicated air pipes positioned at waist height to facilitate coupling and uncoupling from platform level. All train control functions were incorporated in a single 27-way train line which catered for the possible needs of the future.

Opposite page: ***10201 on a goods working at Brockenhurst***
One day in July 1952, 10201 was used to haul a goods from Brockenhurst to Bevois Park sidings, Southampton. 10201 had been removed from the down "Royal Wessex" at Bournemouth the previous evening with "loss of power". I was called to investigate so the following morning it was put on the 3 coach 'school' train to Brockenhurst for observation. The trouble was soon traced to a sticking 'field divert' relay which was quickly rectified, and 10201 completed the diagram to Southampton and back to Bournemouth in time to pick up its normal duty from Bournemouth Central, with the 11.30 from Weymouth.

10202 on Sunday Yeovil Junction - Waterloo stopping train

Six days a week there was a 'Newspaper' train to Exeter, but on Sunday mornings this was curtailed at Yeovil Junction, so the locomotive returned on a stopping train to Waterloo before working the "Bournemouth Belle" both ways. 10202 is leaving Surbiton in the summer of 1953 with a pair of Bulleid three-car corridor sets which at that time were still painted malachite green. The locomotive would already have covered over 4300 miles since the previous Monday morning, and would not be serviced until the next day. The 'Fireman' is standing by the engine room window having nothing else to do!

Opposite page: **Diesel-hauled "Bournemouth Belle"**

10202 was the first to receive its new gears, reducing the top speed to 85 mph, and increasing the maximum tractive effort from 31,000lb to 48,000lb. Here it is seen at the erstwhile Bournemouth West station on a Sunday in September 1953 with the full 12-car train weighing some 485 tons tare. 10202 was in an interim stage of modification, while waiting for equipment for a second stage of field weakening to improve performance.

4EPB (class 415) in service on the South Western Division
5023 enters Clapham Junction bound for Shepperton on a Saturday in July 1953. The first batch of 25 units was allocated to the Western section, and 5023 is in its original state with an inter-unit power jumper. These were later removed, as the maximum accelerating current of an eight car train was close to the rating of a single shoe fuse. Although no-volt relays were fitted, it was found that in certain circumstances equipment did not "drop out" in conductor rail gaps. Later, transistorised relays were fitted, and power jumpers were no longer needed. Note the two different designs of colour light signals; on the SW division, the Westinghouse 1937 manufacture; on the Central division, a post-War design of GEC General Railway Signals.

Opposite page, top: **Ex-LMS Bo-Bo 10800 on loan to the Southern**
In 1952, the Southern Region Operating Department was considering dieselisation of certain secondary lines, and when 827hp 10800 of the LM Region was loaned for a trial, this too came under my wing. 10800 was built by the North British Locomotive Company to LMS specification to handle the type of traffic in the class 3P and 4F steam locomotive categories. 10800 is about to depart from London Bridge platform 9, on 13th August 1952, with a 165-ton train for Tunbridge Wells West via Oxted and East Grinstead (HL), on which I rode both ways. It could cope well enough with this class of work, albeit at no advantage in terms of timings to a class 4 2-6-4 tank. The Paxman 16 RPHXL engine was not an entirely suitable engine for rail traction, and while on the Southern it suffered two major failures.

Opposite page, lower: **10800 at the former East Grinstead 'High Level' station**
10800 stands at the erstwhile East Grinstead 'High Level' with the return train from Tunbridge Wells West on 13th August 1952. Later, it was employed on a 4-leg diagram taking in both Victoria and London Bridge; also Brighton, Horsham and Tunbridge Wells West, working over the Stenying, Oxted and Uckfield lines. The most exacting train was the 15.08 from Victoria to Brighton via Eridge and Uckfield, which had a tight schedule to Eridge. The island platform on the right was used by the Three Bridges trains.

Temporary refuelling arrangements in Waterloo North Sidings

With only four main-line diesel locomotives no attempt was made to provide proper fuelling and daily servicing facilities. Each locomotive needed a daily examination and refuelling, and the photograph shows the ad-hoc arrangements in the North Sidings (site now covered by the new International Terminal) at Waterloo, which existed from September 1951 to August 1955. There was a 4000 gallon tank wagon (on the left) from which fuel oil was fed to each locomotive in turn by the pumps seen in the centre. Lubricating oil was kept in barrels on the platform beside the tank wagon and fed to the engine as required by a semi-rotary hand pump. The tarpaulin was to cover the pumps when not in use. On the day the fuelling was recorded it was dry, but the same work was carried out whether it was fine, raining or snowing! It is surprising that the locomotives performed as well as they did!

The "Royal Wessex" with 10001 at Byfleet & New Haw

The down "Royal Wessex", the 16.35 from Waterloo to Bournemouth and Weymouth, was a diesel turn from the introduction of 10201 in the winter of 1951. Here with its 13-coach 440-ton load, 10001 is seen passing West Weybridge (now Byfleet & New Haw) on Whitsun Saturday 1953. Motive power was at a premium this weekend as the breakage of a driving axle on Merchant Navy 35020 at Crewkerne on 24 March 1953 had resulted in all Merchant Navy and West Country Pacifics being withdrawn in turn over a period of weeks for ultrasonic testing. All four diesels were at work replacing eight steam locomotives and performed impeccably. Note the complete train is in Carmine and Cream ("Blood and Custard") livery and, with the exception of the Restaurant cars - a modified Bulleid 'Tavern Car' pair in the rear 7-coach Bournemouth West portion, is composed of BR Mk1 stock.

10000 with the "Bournemouth Belle" at Bournemouth West

After two years of reasonably successful operation of 10201/2, the Railway Executive decided that it would be advantageous to bring 10000/1 together with them as the Southern had the better maintenance set up. The LMS twins were transferred to the Southern, and two further 4-leg diagrams were introduced on the SW Division. Here 10000 waits for the road with the up "Bournemouth Belle" from Bournemouth West on a Sunday in August 1954. By this time, improved bearings had been fitted, and the engine uprated to 1750hp giving more or less equal performance to the Southern locomotives.

*Above: **New 2EPB on the South London line***

In 1953, it was decided that 10-car trains would be introduced on the South Eastern suburban lines, and new 2-car units to a BR "standard" design were built at Eastleigh to provide the extra length. To enable the old converted 1909 former ac 2-car units to be retired, the first batch of 8 new units, 5701-8 designated 2EPB, was allocated to the South London line and took over in September 1954. Four more worked the Wimbledon-West Croydon services. Seen passing Peckham Rye depot between Denmark Hill and Peckham Rye on a Victoria-London Bridge working in March 1955, these units were similar in layout to the SR design 2EPBs.

*Above: **10203 on first trial run at Crowborough in March 1954***
The third Southern main-line diesel-electric locomotive was delayed while BR Headquarters tried to decide if it should be of a different design. In the meantime, the English Electric Company had introduced a Mk2 2000 hp version of their 16SVT engine with four valve heads and a modified governor, giving continuous speed and power regulation between idling and maximum speed. While there were minor changes to the mechanical parts, the power equipment was revised with a lighter main generator, six-pole traction motors and new control gear. Maximum speed was 90 mph and maximum tractive effort 50,000lb. New construction at Ashford had ceased by then so 10203 was built at Brighton, and is seen standing at Crowborough on its initial trial run in March 1954.

*Opposite page, lower: **2EPB on North London line service entering North Woolwich***
In 1959, a further batch of 34 2EPBs using former 2NOL underframes was introduced. Intended primarily for the Waterloo-Windsor/Weybridge services, they replaced the wood-bodied 2NOLS. With graffiti on the front end, class 416, 6313 (formerly 5613) is approaching North Woolwich on a North London line service from Richmond in July 1985. After the closure of Broad Street, and extension of the third rail from Dalston to North Woolwich, the Southern Region provided these 2EPBs to work the services for which window bars had to be fitted, changing over for maintenance at Richmond. Subsequently they were replaced by class 313 25kV ac/750V dc units.

10203 with other rolling stock at Willesden for IRCA Exhibition
In May/June 1954, an exhibition of the latest BR and LT rolling stock was held in the roundhouse of Willesden Motive Power Depot for delegates to the International Railway Congress Association Convention in London, and the general public. 10203 had barely settled down to a service routine when it was returned to Brighton Works to be prepared for the exhibition. Other "Southern" exhibits were the motor coach of BR design 2EPB 5707 and BR class 4 2-6-4T 80084 - also built at Brighton. 10203 ran from Brighton to Willesden, hauling 80084 via Selhurst where 5707 was picked up, then via the West London Extension line. There was a minor incident at Selhurst when one pony truck of 10203 was derailed on some rather dubious pointwork. There was no damage and the pony truck was soon re-railed!

Opposite page: **10203 and test train at the erstwhile Tunbridge Wells West station**
The following day, 10203 worked a 10-coach train to Tunbridge Wells West and back. Here, it is waiting to be coupled to its train at Tunbridge Wells West prior to returning to Brighton. Note the different arrangement of louvres for the greater volume of air required. Even with a larger Ashford-designed train-heating boiler of 1500 lb/hr output, the total weight was reduced to 132.8 tons (10201/2 were 134.8 tons). Following these runs 10203 was transferred to Nine Elms, and was soon working on both the Bournemouth and West of England lines. Among other duties was the up "Royal Wessex" from Bournemouth West and the down "Atlantic Coast Express".

10203 leaving Waterloo on the "Atlantic Coast Express"
Following the Willesden exhibition, 10203 returned to its former 4-leg diagram and is leaving Waterloo platform 11 with the "Atlantic Coast Express" on Saturday 14th August 1954. This is the main train, and was loaded to 13 coaches. The second portion with twelve coaches stands in platform 10 behind Merchant Navy 35023.

An Engineer on the Southern Diesels and Electrics

10203 on the 1 p.m. Waterloo to Exeter Central. 22 June 1955.

11 coaches = 365 tons tare: 385 tons gross to Templecombe. 9 coaches = 301 tons gross: 315 tons to Exeter Central.

Distance Miles	Point	Schedule	Actual Mins Secs	Speed	Notes
0.0	**WATERLOO**		0.000		
1.3	Vauxhall		2.59	46	
3.9	Clapham Junction	7	6.24	49/38	40 pws
5.6	Earlsfield		8.43	51	
7.3	Wimbledon		10.32	56	
8.7	Raynes Park		11.57	61	
9.8	New Malden		13.02	61	
11.0	Berrylands		14.12	62	
12.0	Surbiton		15.11	63	
13.3	Hampton Court Junction	18	16.22	69	
14.4	Esher		17.18	69	
15.9	Hersham		18.32	72	
17.1	Walton		19.32	69	
18.1	Oatlands		20.26	67	
19.1	Weybridge		21.19	68	
20.4	Byfleet & New Haw		22.26	73	
21.7	West Byfleet		23.29	69	
23.0	MP 23		24.4	63	
24.4	**WOKING**	29	26.51		
0.0	**WOKING**		0.00		
0.4	Woking Junction		1.23		
3.6	Brookwood		5.38	54	
6.6	MP 31		8.45		pws
7.8	Sturt Lane Junction		11.10		
8.8	Farnborough		12.53	43	
12.1	Fleet		16.17	64/70	
16.3	Winchfield		19.13	68	
17.8	Hook		21.16	72	
19.3	Newnham Siding		22.31	73	
23.4	Basingstoke		26.01	61	eased
25.9	Worting Junction	29	28.15	64	
26.6	MP 51		28.59	62	
28.0	Oakley		30.11	62	

Distance Miles	Point	Schedule	Actual Mins Secs	Speed	Notes
29.1	MP 53½			31.13	63
31.2	Overton		33.02	69	
34.8	Whitchurch		36.05	73	
36.7	Hurctbourne		37.36	77	
38.3	MP 62½		38.49	74	
42.0	**ANDOVER JUNCTION**	45	42.42		
0.0	**ANDOVER JUNCTION**		0.00		
1.3	Red Post Junction		2.69	39	
2.8	MP 69		4.38	59	
4.8	MP 71		6.42	57	
6.3	Grateley		8.23	54	
7.1	MP 73		9.07½	54	
9.2	Amesbury Junction		11.16	69	
11.8	Porton		13.27	76/79	
16.2	Tunnel Junction	18½	19.19	14	pws
17.3	**SALISBURY**	21	22.02		
0.0	**SALISBURY**		0.00		
1.5	MP 85		3.30	34	
2.5	Wilton		5.06	42	pws
5.5	MP 89		8.27	54	
8.3	Dinton		11.10	66	
12.6	Tisbury		15.10	67	
15.5	MP 99		17.33½	66	
16.5	MP 100		18.29½	61	
17.6	Semley		19.39	59	
21.7	Gillingham		23.10	79/60	pws
24.0	MP 107½		25.28	55	
26.1	Abbey Ford		27.14	81/15	pws
28.5	**TEMPLECOMBE**	34	32.03		
0.0	**TEMPLECOMBE**		0.00		
0.5	MP 112½		1.44	30	
1.5	MP 113½		3.26	39	
2.4	Millborne Port		4.31	61/78	
6.1	**SHERBOURNE**	11	8.27		

An Engineer on the Southern Diesels and Electrics

Distance Miles	Point	Schedule	Actual Mins Secs	Speed	Notes
0.0	**SHERBOURNE**		0.00		
2.7	Wyke Crossing		4.03	61	
4.6	**YEOVIL JUNCTION**	8	6.55		
0.0	**YEOVIL JUNCTION**		0.00		
0.6	MP 123¼		1.58	36	
1.6	MP 124¼		3.27	44	
2.2	Sutton Bingham		4.14	47	
2.6	MP 125¼		4.43½	49	
3.6	MP 126¼		5.54	52	
5.3	Hardingham Siding		7.28	70/78	
8.8	Crewkerne		10.15	70	
9.6	MP 132¼		11.01½	64	
10.6	MP 133¼		12.03½	56	
11.4	Hewish Crossing		12.49	69/80	
16.8	Chard Junction	16.56	79/15	pws	
21.9	Axminster		21.57	42/65	
25.2	Seaton Junction		25.19	59	
26.8	MP 149½		27.09½	52	
27.8	MP 150½		28.22½	48	
28.8	MP 151½		29.40½	45	
29.8	MP 152½		31.02	44	
30.8	MP 153½		32.18	51	eased
32.1	Honiton		33.33	68/77	
36.7	Sidmouth Junction		37.16	72	
37.6	MP 160¼		38.05	73	
38.6	MP 161¼		36.56	68	
40.5	Whimple		40.24	73	
44.1	Broad Clyst		43.17	77	
46.0	Pinhoe		44.51	69/66	
47.8	Exmouth Junction	52	46.34	10	signals
48.9	**EXETER CENTRAL**	55	49.53		

10203 on the down "Golden Arrow" near Petts Wood Junction

As with 10202, 10203 spent a week on the South Eastern Division working the "Golden Arrow" and "Night Ferry". 10203 approaches Petts Wood Junction on 16th February 1955 with the down "Golden Arrow". On this occasion, George Weedon, Motive Power Officer, and Dick Hardy, then District Motive Power Officer at Stewarts Lane, travelled on the locomotive, and instructed the driver to work the train "heavy" with the result that 11 minutes were clipped off the schedule, much to the chagrin of the Pullman Car staff! The "Night Ferry" with five or more 55 ton Wagons Lits sleeping cars was a heavy train, and was normally double headed by a West Country and an L1 class 4-4-0, but 10203 could cope with it easily.

Diagrams (workings) for the five prototype diesels on Southern Region
(First three from March 1953)

No 1

Monday to Saturday

0125 Waterloo to Exeter Central

0730 Exeter Central to Waterloo (refuel)

1300 Waterloo to Exeter Central

1755 Exeter Central to Waterloo.

Sunday

0135 Waterloo to Yeovil Junction

0710 Yeovil Junction to Waterloo (refuel)

1230 Waterloo to Bournemouth West ("Bournemouth Belle")

1634 Bournemouth West to Waterloo ("Bournemouth Belle")

2054 Waterloo to Southampton Terminus

0110 Southampton Terminus to Waterloo, then to Nine Elms for maintenance, then to diagram 2.

No 2

Tuesday to Saturday

0540 Waterloo to Weymouth

1130 Weymouth to Waterloo (refuel)

1635 Waterloo to Weymouth ("Royal Wessex")

2155 Weymouth to Southampton Terminus

0110 Southampton Terminus to Waterloo

Sunday

To Nine Elms for maintenance, then to diagram 1

No 3

Monday to Friday

0830 Waterloo to Weymouth

1325 Weymouth to Waterloo (refuel)

1800 Waterloo to Exeter Central

2240 Exmouth Junction to Nine Elms (fitted freight)

Sunday

0930 Waterloo to Bournemouth West

1420 Bournemouth West to Waterloo

No 4 (from March 1954)

0240 Waterloo to Bournemouth West

0720 Bournemouth West to Waterloo ("Royal Wessex") (refuel)

1100 Waterloo to Exeter Central ("Atlantic Coast Express")

1630 Exeter Central to Waterloo

(As far as possible, No. 10203 was kept to this diagram.)

The fifth locomotive was run to a steam diagram on weekdays, usually the
0930 Waterloo to Bournemouth West and 1420 return.

1004 in new inspection Shed/Diesel Depot at St Leonards
For maintenance and cleaning of the new stock, purpose-built installations were provided at Bulverhive, east of St Leonards, adjacent to the Hastings-Eastbourne line. Prior to opening, the depot was inspected by Member of the BTC for Engineering, Sir J Landale Train. Waiting for the official party unit 1004 stands inside the new depot. The Southern's Electric Rolling Stock Maintenance Engineer, Frank Muncey, inspects the pit lighting, an innovation on the Region in 1957! An overhead crane was installed so that engines could be changed and sent away to Eastleigh for overhaul so enhancing stock availability.

Opposite page, top: ***The first "Hastings" six-car diesel-electric Unit 1001***
The 'fifties saw considerable pressure from regular business travellers on the Hastings direct line for improvements to schedules and rolling stock. 32 new coaches were ordered, but at the same time, a ninety-minute journey time was the aim for the best trains. The Schools class, then thirty years old, and the largest permitted between Tunbridge Wells and Bopeep Junction, did not by then have the capacity to work reliably to faster schedules. Electrification was, at the time, out of the question, so the Assistant Electrical Engineer, H S Smyth, proposed "diesel-electrification" which was accepted in principle. English Electric had produced some very successful diesel-electric trains for the Egyptian State Railways and as the engine/generator sets in Mk 2 form were suitable, the order for new coaches was increased to 42, and 14 were built as diesel-electric power cars. At Basingstoke in January 1957, the first 1000hp 6-car unit 1001 is on a trial run from Eastleigh. Note the two 500hp power cars and "short" vehicles built on the 56ft 11in underframes originally intended for steam haulage

Opposite page, lower: ***1003 at Bournemouth West after a run from Waterloo***
The Hastings dieselisation was carried out in two phases. The first phase was introduced with the Summer timetable of 1957, with seven units built on 56ft 11in underframes and 3 units on standard length 63ft 5in underframes. During the run-up period a demonstration non-stop run was made on 25th February 1957, between Waterloo and Bournemouth West, with unit 1003 carrying the Regional General Manager and senior officers. Here, unit 1003 is at Bournemouth West after arrival from Waterloo. Unfortunately 'Murphy' was at work and one traction motor armature bearing collapsed in the later stage of the run, so the return trip was cancelled. Motors were identical to those on electric multiple unit stock, eg EE507s, where a bearing failure was almost unknown!

Two "Hampshire" 2-car diesel-electric units at Eastleigh

Dieselisation of the services radiating from Southampton had been promoted before the Hastings scheme, but due to the urgency of the latter, the "Hampshire Area" scheme took second place. 18x500hp 2-car units1101-18 were built at Eastleigh in 1957, immediately following the first ten 6-car units for Hastings Stage 1, to work services from Southampton and Portsmouth to Salisbury, Andover and Alton. The design was based on the electric 2EPB but with a composite driving trailer with toilets. The power equipment was identical to the "Hastings" units. Units 1103 and 1104 are on their initial acceptance run in May 1957, waiting to return to the Carriage Works. Four more units 1119-22, were built for Hastings-Ashford services.

Opposite page, top: **Hampshire 2-car diesel-electric unit leaving Eastleigh.**

The Hampshire services were introduced in stages in the summer of 1957, and proved popular right from the start. A "clock face" timetable was introduced, and schedule times were improved. So popular were they that an extra second-class trailer coach had to be added for most services, and the engines up-rated to 600hp to maintain the same schedules. Seen here is an Andover Junction-Portsmouth service operated by 2-car unit 1113 in March 1958. One notable mechanical difference from electric multiple unit stock was the use of buckeye couplers between the coaches. This was to make operation more flexible. Note the tall semaphore signal and the erecting shop of the former Eastleigh Locomotive Works in the background.

Opposite page, lower: **First stage 2 "Hastings" long unit 1014 at Eastleigh**

The "Hastings" Stage 2 stock followed immediately after the 18 2-car units for the Hampshire services. Here 6L unit 1014, the first for Stage 2, is being prepared at Eastleigh Carriage Works on a Saturday morning in February 1958, for its acceptance run to Romsey and back, which I accompanied. All of these vehicles were built on 63ft 5in underframes - the standard length then adopted by BR for main line vehicles. Carriage building ceased at Eastleigh in 1963, and repairs were moved to part of the Locomotive Works. The site is now an industrial estate.

Prototype 4-car 4CEP "Express" unit on trial at Earlswood

In anticipation of future requirements, six new all-steel main line units were built at Eastleigh to BR designs in 1956. These were four 4-car corridor units, numbered 7101-4, and two 4-car Buffet units, numbered 7001-2. They were an updated version of the 4COR and 4BUF, stock and the interiors were finished with wood-veneer panelling. Traction equipment was based on the 4EPBs with two EE507 motors of 250hp (1-hour) in each motor bogie, geared for a maximum speed of 90 mph. Single-bolster bogies and running gear conformed to BR standards of the time. This stock was allocated to the Central Division, but before being put into service, a series of tests was run, and here 7103 has just arrived at Earlswood on a brake test from Selhurst in July 1957. Two of my former colleagues, the late Cyril Frost and the late Tommy Russ are on the train.

An Engineer on the Southern Diesels and Electrics

'Modern' motive power on display at Battersea Wharf
In the early days of 'Modernisation' of the railways, several exhibitions of the then new rolling stock were staged. This one, at Battersea Wharf, was in conjunction with an International Conference and, after being shown to the delegates, was opened to the public. On show were from left to right, a then new 350hp diesel-electric shunter No. 13354, the first of the English Electric Type 1 Bo-Bo locomotives No. D8000, and the prototype English Electric 'Deltic'. Behind the Type 1 was a 'new' Hastings diesel-electric Power Car. It is worth noting that each of the exhibits had power equipment designed and manufactured by the former English Electric Company, one of many UK rolling stock firms, which has since 'gone to the wall'.

Swiss Federal Railways Ae 6/6 Co-Co electric locomotive
When the decision was taken to build some powerful Bo-Bo electric locomotives for the Kent Coast electrification, BR were employing 'Industrial Designers', and all new rolling stock was subject to scrutiny by a 'Design Panel', that had been established in 1956. The locomotive illustrated is one of 125 Co-Co electric locomotives of the Swiss Federal Railways built between 1952 and 1958, and seen at Winterthur on a train of road stone. The Southern Region hoped to model their new Bo-Bo electric locomotives on this design, because it was a pleasing shape and relatively easy to build with straight sides and plain curvature between the cab front and body sides. To justify their existence the industrial designers interfered in the design, and the shape of the locomotives was different and more expensive!

First Doncaster-built 2552 hp Bo-Bo booster locomotive
The first of the new Bo-Bo 750 volt third-rail mixed-traffic electric locomotives for the Kent Coast electrification stands outside the 1915 Durnsford Road Inspection shed on 29th December 1958. Note the rather flat front and the compound curvature between the cab and curved bodysides - an expensive shape to produce in steel. The control gear for these locomotives was a logical development of the earlier Co-Co locomotives. A single motor-generator booster set fed four fully-suspended traction motors with a total 1-hour shaft hp rating of 2552 (2500hp at the rail) on a weight of only 77 tons (78.5 tonnes). Starting tractive effort was 43,000 lb and the top speed 90 mph. They could haul 900 ton freight trains on a gradient of 1 in 70, and 500 ton passenger trains at 80 mph on the level. The centrally-mounted pantograph was for the 750 volt overhead installed in the principal freight yards of the SE Division. Train heating was fed by the jumper inside the RH, buffer, and there were air and vacuum brake pipes. 24 locomotives were built at Doncaster.

Opposite page: ***New Electric Locomotive Maintenance Depot at Stewarts Lane***
New maintenance depots were provided for the Kent Coast multiple unit stock at Stewarts Lane and Ramsgate with a new Overhaul Shop at Ashford (Chart Leacon). Electric (and later diesel) locomotives were maintained separately from multiple unit stock in a new Electric Locomotive inspection shed, built adjacent to the SE main line. The second locomotive, E5001, is waiting to be commissioned. The shed was divided into two parts, one for routine maintenance, equipped with overhead conductors for moving and testing locomotives, the other dealing with heavy parts and wheel re-profiling. E5001 stands under the overhead crane in February 1959.

Training trip with E5001 at Gillingham, Kent.
Driver training was initially carried out on the SE Division between Stewarts Lane and Gillingham with whatever stock was available. Here E5001, having just run round its train, is entering the up platform at Gillingham before returning to London in April 1959. This train was formed of 10 coaches, and was accompanied by Charles Klapper, editor of the erstwhile paper "Modern Transport." He and another guest, Eric Fry, now a Vice-President of the Railway Correspondence and Travel Society (RCTS) were impressed by the sustained speed of 66 mph up the 1 in 100 grade of Sole Street Bank. Note the miscellaneous collection of rolling stock; the filthy state of the tracks; protection boarding on the up line removed for conductor rail replacement and flat bottom rail on the down line, with an early experimental form of rail fastening.

Opposite Page: E5002 on 14-coach test train at Newhaven Harbour
The booster sets on the first two locomotives had duplex wave windings, and commutation problems arose, due to current imbalance between the two armature windings. The remainder were built with conventional lap windings, and the first two were rewound. E5002 is in platform 2, having just arrived at Newhaven Harbour in March 1959, on a 14-coach (464 tons tare) test run from Victoria. The object was to work the locomotive hard to check the commutation of the new machine, which was satisfactory. The Chief Traction Machine Designer of the erstwhile English Electric Company, the late Dennis Lightband, is standing close to the locomotive.

E5003 using overhead current collection at Hither Green
Through freight, as well as passengers, had been the raison d'etre of the Dover-Dunkuerque train ferries in the late 1930s. Perishables, mainly fruit, were important cargoes from both Spain and Italy. Before October 1960, trains went on to Ewer Street, Southwark. Transfer to and from Hither Green via London Bridge and Borough Market Junction was by steam locomotives, normally outside peak hours. Just prior to the opening of the new depot at Hither Green, a train originating from Ewer Street is about to depart from the down sidings for Dover and the train Ferry. Vacuum brake was still being used at this time (June 1962), and as it was only used on this side of the Channel vehicles often arrived with defective brakes, so speed had to be limited for the brake power available. Some 25 ton bogie brake vans later had air pipes and emergency valves fitted, and trains were then worked on the air brake

Opposite page, top: **E5000 on a heavy coal train at Shakespeare Cliff, Dover.**
Phase 2 came into operation in June 1962, when all freight traffic was handed over to diesel or electric haulage, the majority of the heavier trains being handled by electric locomotives. On a fine day in August 1962, E5000 had just arrived at the eastern portal of Shakespeare Cliff Tunnel with a heavy train (about 900 tons), mainly coal from the former Betteshanger Colliery. The first seven vehicles were provided for additional brake power on the 1 in 60-70 down grades approaching Buckland Junction, the remainder of the train being formed of 25x32 ton steel coal wagons. The dust was blown up by the cooling air discharged from the traction motors. Note the semaphore signals, the Continental Ferry vans behind the down line and the flat bottom rail on the up line.

Opposite page, lower: **Up "Night Ferry" near Factory Junction with E5002**
By 1959, the "Night Ferry" included sleeping cars from both Paris and Brussels, and in the height of the season could load up to 10 Wagons Lits sleepers and five BR coaches plus two or three baggage vans, totalling 800 tons tare, or probably as much as 850 tons with passengers and baggage. The up train is passing Factory Junction in June 1960, hauled by E5002 with seven Wagons Lits and the tare weight would have been about 650 tons. At this time the ìNight Ferryî was routed via Chatham and the Catford Loop. Note the flat bottom rail on all three running lines and the next two tracks on the down gradient giving access to Stewarts Lane depot

Test train at Folkestone Junction Reversing Sidings

Just prior to the opening of Phase 2 of the Kent Coast electrification, tests to establish or confirm the safe operation of trains on Folkestone Bank, 1 in 30, were undertaken on a suitably damp day in May 1962. E5010, coupled to a train of multiple unit stock comprising a motor luggage van and two 4CEP units, has just arrived at Folkestone Junction sidings from Folkestone Harbour. E5010 had a struggle with this load of some 337 tons, and almost slipped to a stand near the top of the bank, being saved by cutting in the EMU stock! The use of electric locomotives over the branch was unlikely but their capability had to be established.

E5015 about to leave Victoria with the "Golden Arrow"

Only two named trains survived the Kent Coast electrification, the "Golden Arrow" and "Night Ferry". The 'Night Ferry' had been electrically-hauled since the inception of Stage 1, and the "Golden Arrow" from the inauguration of Phase 2 on 18 June 1962, although in the interim, diesel haulage had been introduced. The "Arrow" could load to 10 Pullmans and two "Utility" vans, with a tare weight of 425 tons, and was timed to Dover in 80 minutes. By 1963 "economies" had reduced the formation of the "Arrow" to six or seven Pullman cars and two or three BR corridors, as seen in this photograph with E5015 at the head in June 1963. In common with steam practice, it was usual to keep a dedicated locomotive, always immaculately clean, for the "Arrow"; the same locomotive also worked the "Night Ferry." At this time the "Arrow" had an early afternoon departure so there was ample time for cleaning between release from the "Night Ferry" and attachment to the "Arrow."

Special test train with Southern Region CME staff at Minster.
In March 1961, a 4CEP was employed on a test train, and the passengers were CM&EE department staff. This was one of the later Phase 2 units, 7163. The single bolster BR 'standard' bogies of the Phase 1 units rode so badly at speed, that the CM&EE, H.H.Swift, issued an ultimatum to BR Central Staff. He would himself issue instructions to revert to the former Southern Railway bogie design which, if not perfect, at least rode better than the BR design. BR instead substituted Commonwealth cast steel trailer bogies. This added some 7 tons to the tare weight of a 4-car unit and, while it gave some improvement, higher rotational stiffness led to premature flange wear!

Opposite page, top: ***Train of 2HAP units passing Factory Junction***
Stopping and semi-fast services for the Kent Coast electrification were covered by 2-car units, similar in concept to the pre-war 2HALs. There were two versions for Phases 1 and 2, known as 2HAPs (2-car, half-lavatory, EP brake) which were built to BR standards of the time for all-steel stock. The Phase 1 batch had BR single-bolster bogies, but Commonwealth bogies were used at the inner ends of cars for Phase 2. Motors and control gear followed that for the "express" stock, and they were geared for a maximum speed of 90 mph. Here, four units on a Victoria-Faversham-Ramsgate/Dover stopping train are approaching Factory Junction in June 1960.

Opposite page, lower: ***BR/Derby Type 2 on loan to the Southern Region***
The new EMU maintenance depot at Ramsgate occupied the site of the former steam motive power depot. To enable the latter to be closed 15 BR/Derby type 2s were 'borrowed' from the LM Region in 1959. New diesel-electric locomotives (D6500 series, type 3) had been ordered, but as authorization by BR had been delayed, the first did not arrive on the Region until December 1959. Here, D5002 is seen approaching Minster (Thanet) in March 1961, on a stopping train from Ashford via Canterbury West. For maintenance purposes, they were allocated to Hither Green and used at first almost entirely in the Ashford-Dover-Ramsgate-Canterbury-Faversham area.

An Engineer on the Southern Diesels and Electrics

N Class 2-6-0 of Southern Railway at Eastleigh

This photograph has special significance because the Southern (really SE&CR) Maunsell N class was one of a total of 157 (80 N class) 2-6-0 general purpose locomotives, that did stalwart work over all parts of the Southern Railway. Under "Modernisation" the Southern needed a locomotive of equivalent utility. The 157 Moguls were produced over a period of 17 years, from 1916; 50 'N' class came as sets of parts from Woolwich Arsenal after World War 1. More sets of parts went to the Irish and Metropolitan Railways, the latter being built into 2-6-4 tank locomotives. The Regional engineers evolved a specification for a diesel which fell between BR types B and C; a Bo-Bo air-braked locomotive weighing around 75 tons, that could develop at least 1000hp at the rail; one that could heat passenger trains by electricity; and a locomotive that could haul electric multiple-unit stock in the event of a major area power failure. Sulzer had proposed equipping a BR type 2 with an eight-cylinder engine, but Derby could see no use for it!

Opposite page, top: **Ruston 275 hp 0-6-0 diesel-electric shunter at Southampton Docks.**
Shunting in Southampton Docks had been in the hands of former USA Transportation Corps 0-6-0 tanks since 1947; built for a short life, they were becoming expensive to maintain. The wheelbase of the standard 350/400hp diesel-electric shunters was too long for many of the curves in the "old" docks. A suitable locomotive was found in a "standard" Ruston product - their 275hp 0-6-0 diesel-electric. With AEI electrical equipment and a Paxman 6RPH engine, it was a good choice. Some small modifications were made, for example the addition of vacuum (and later air) brakes, marker lights and lamp brackets, and shunters' steps. D2987 is in Southampton Docks in 1960.

Opposite page, lower: **Swiss Federal Railways SLM/Sulzer Bo-Bo - inspiration for the BR Type 3?**
The Swiss Federal Railways class Am 4/4, of which two had been built in 1938, to a lightweight design of 65 tons by the Swiss Locomotive Company with Oerlikon electrical equipment were intended for use on lines that were not electrified, and which penetrated foreign territory, for example from Geneva to La Plaine in France, and from Winterthur to Singen in Germany. An eight-cylinder in-line Sulzer LDA28 engine of 1200hp was coupled to a dc traction generator which, in the same frame, had a dc generator to supply train heating. By 1957 the updated engine was rated at 1550hp, and even allowing for around 135 kW (180 hp) for train heating, the power at the wheel treads would still be over 1000hp. The advantage of electric transmission is that the <u>total</u> output of the engine is regulated so when train heating is not required, the extra output is automatically available for traction. I had been introduced to this locomotive first in May 1955, on a visit to the Sulzer works in Winterthur, and rode on the locomotive as far as Seuzach, two stops from Winterthur.

Three locomotives for track force tests at Three Bridges.

In 1961, the question arose as to whether fully-suspended traction motors should continue to be adopted for high speeds. With line speeds being increased to 100mph, the Permanent Way Engineers were concerned about possible damage to track. At Horley, on the Brighton line, the Research Department had installed some load-sensitive recording baseplates and a series of comparisons was made between various types of rolling stock, both multiple units and locomotives. Because at the time the Southern Region had the only electric locomotives with fully-suspended traction motors, one (E5005) was used in comparison with a class 33, D6506, and a Co-Co electric locomotive, 20001. The three are seen at Three Bridges in May 1961 prior to their runs over the test section at speeds of 85, 75 and 90 mph respectively. The results were misleading, as they appeared to indicate that vertical forces were more or less proportional to axle load, irrespective of the type of motor suspension, and led to the disastrous adoption of nose-suspended traction motors on the AL6 (class 86).

Opposite page: SR Type 3 (class 33) at Hornsey on train of electrically-heated stock.

The result was the BRCW/Sulzer type 3, later class 33. The first order was for 65 locomotives, but due to delays in convincing BR central staff of what was needed, ordering, (and in turn delivery) was delayed, the first locomotive D6500 arriving on the Region just before Christmas 1959 - six months after the inauguration of Phase 1 of the Kent Coast electrification. When production got underway, type 3s arrived at the rate of one per week. The initial order was increased first to 86, then to 98, the last 12 locomotives being built to the "Hastings" line loading gauge. They were very useful and adaptable locomotives, and if one could not cope with a particular working, two in multiple could. When BR finally decided to adopt electric train heating - very necessary for the West Coast Main Line electrification - a class 33 was borrowed in January 1963, and sent to Derby for static tests, then, in February, to the East Coast main line for trials between Kings Cross and Edinburgh. D6504 is at Hornsey with a rake of seven Mk1 coaches. An eighth coach was added from Southern Region stock.

Fawley-Bromford Bridge oil tak train leaving Fawley

One of the early inter-Region workings of class 33s was on oil tank trains between Fawley refinery and Bromford Bridge in north east Birmingham. This traffic was previously worked by class 9 2-10-0s, and a small batch was allocated to Eastleigh for the purpose. It was originally suggested that these trains would need two class 33s in multiple, but I disagreed and accompanied one train as far as Didcot to check and to demonstrate to the Western Region people that one class 33 was sufficient. Originally routed via the former Didcot, Newbury and Southampton line, Worcester and Lickey, closure of the line between Shawford and Didcot led to diversion via Reading. Here D6533 is about to depart from Fawley on 30th May 1963.

Opposite page: **Air-braked seven-car set 900 and Class 33 D6529 at Eridge**

In September 1963, to supplement the 19 new diesel-electric multiple units, and until electrically-heated locomotive-hauled stock could be made available, some redundant electric multiple unit vehicles were used for an extra peak hour service between Tunbridge Wells West and London Bridge. With little modification only involving replacement of the motor bogie, the fitting of a motor generator set, and re-connection of the lighting and heating circuits, a set of seven coaches was made up from withdrawn 2BIL 2006 and five all-steel trailer coaches from withdrawn suburban stock. The motor coach of 2006 was at one end, and the driving trailer at the other end, providing accommodation for the guard at each end of the set, which was numbered 900. The motor generator set and heating were fed from the locomotive and the automatic air brakes of the ex-EMU stock were used without modification. D6529 is berthing its train at Eridge after working the 17.20 London Bridge-Tunbridge Wells West in September 1963. It was used for four years and was withdrawn after a fire in September 1967

Class 33 on Western Section freight train near Pirbright
1963 saw the allocation of a number of class 33s to the SW Division for both passenger and freight. They began working some of the Waterloo-Bournemouth passenger trains together with freight between Feltham and Southampton, as well as Ocean Liner Boat trains. Seen in the deep cutting (Deepcut) near Pirbright, D6536 is at the head of a freight train from Southampton to Feltham on a Saturday in April 1964. Conductor rails then went only as far as Sturt Lane Junction where they were fed by a substation also feeding the Frimley line. There was one electric working per day, which used the flat Sturt Lane Junction (since removed) between the main and Frimley lines.

Opposite page: **Class 33 on acceptance test train entering Tonbridge**
Delivered at a rate of one each week, each class 33 had an acceptance run to Dover and back, before being signed off from the builder. D6548 is hauling the eight coach "restriction 1" set (ex SE Division 8ft 6in wide stock), dedicated to this duty and normally berthed at Grove Park, approaching Tonbridge on its acceptance run in April 1961. The conductor rails are in position but as yet uncharged, and both tracks have recently been relaid with new flat bottom rail and realigned to raise the speed restriction from 40 to 50 mph.

The first narrow-body Class 33 at Maidstone East

In 1962, the Hastings direct line (Tunbridge Wells to Bopeep Junction) was still restricted by sub-standard clearances, and to eliminate steam completely, it was necessary to provide a handful of diesel locomotives of reduced width. The last twelve locomotives of class 33 were built with bodies narrower by 8³/₄in. These locomotives also worked away from the Hastings direct line but worked all freight and van traffic over the line, until electrification in 1987. Dubbed "Slim Jims", D6586 is at Maidstone East in August, about to couple to a pick-up goods for Ashford on which I travelled. The driver invited me to take the controls between Harrietsham and Charing. The narrower profile is immediately apparent.

The first 1600 hp electro-diesel prototype on test at Eastleigh.

As long ago as 1944, the Southern's engineers had been investigating the use of an electric locomotive with auxiliary power to avoid having to provide either conductor rails or overhead wires in sidings. The idea began with a scheme for a booster electric shunting locomotive, with auxiliary battery power, which I drafted while in the drawing office at Deepdene. This gravitated to a small electric locomotive with either an auxiliary gas turbine, or a diesel engine and eventually to a full-blown electric locomotive of 1600hp, with a 600hp auxiliary engine - the E6000 series or class 73. Six prototypes were authorised in 1959, for which I was what today would be called the 'Project Engineer'. They were erected in the erstwhile Eastleigh Carriage Works because, to keep weight to a minimum, certain carriage body techniques were employed. The first, E6001, is at Eastleigh about to depart on diesel power for its first run to Fareham and back in January 1962. The performance specification was the same as for the class 33, but the inherent characteristics of an electric locomotive gave the class 73 more short-time power at the rail in the lower speed range.

The first electro-diesel E6001 on a 700 ton test train at Hither Green

The class 73s are resistance controlled - reliable dc choppers were not available in the early 1960s - and for flexibility the resistances were well-ventilated with a generous margin for heating. The specification called for the haulage of freight trains of 700 tons on a gradient of 1 in 60, and in March 1962, a test train was made up at Hither Green for a return trip to Ashford via Otford and Maidstone East. Between Maidstone East and Bearsted there are $1^{1}/_{2}$ miles of 1 in 60. The reverse direction has nothing steeper than 1 in 100, apart from a short 1 in 75 on the up loop at Chislehurst. It was a dull rather damp day and apart from a little wheelslip on Bearsted bank, the performance was excellent. E6001 is about to leave Hither Green for Ashford.

E6001 about to leave Hither Green with 700 ton test train

This is another view of E6001 at Hither Green alongside one of its more powerful sisters, E5022, which has its pantograph raised ready to depart with a main line freight via Tonbridge. Note the quite extensive overhead installation, not required with electro-diesel locomotives. I travelled on E6001 on both trips, and was well satisfied with the performance.

"Reading" 3-car diesel-electric Unit 205026 at Worting Junction
The success of the Hampshire area diesel scheme encouraged its extension, and 11 additional 3-car units (1123-33) were built between 1960 and 1962 to cover services between Portsmouth and Reading. Previously, four 2-car units were built to work between Hastings and Ashford and on the Bexhill West branch (since closed). Similar to the earlier units, former "Reading" unit 1126, now 205026, is passing Worting Junction on a Reading-Portsmouth service in 1985 in the later BR blue and off-white livery. The up Bournemouth line is on the embankment, and the two non-electrified tracks of the Salisbury line are between the train and the embankment.

Opposite page: **E6003 newly arrived from Eastleigh via Lancing with passenger stock**
All six prototype electro-diesels were completed by the middle of 1962 and after the first two the painting style of BR "electric" green was enhanced by a wide strip of light grey along the bottom of the body sides. These are very flexible locomotives and can handle light trains under diesel power, multiple with another of the same type under diesel or electric power, multiple with a class 33 and with electric multiple units. E6003 is at Stewarts Lane in April 1962, with a short train which includes the prototype BR compartment coach with a RGF body built at Eastleigh. Note the retracted collector shoes. E6003 is preserved in working order by the Electro Diesel Locomotive Group of which I was invited to be the President.

SNCF 68000 class A1A-A1A at Paris Gare St Lazare in May 1964

This photograph was taken during my two weeks with CCM (Compangnie Construction Méchanique - Procédés Sulzer), to study manufacture of the LVA24 range of engines in their works at Mantes (Seine). French Railways - SNCF - had ordered 81 locomotives of 2700 hp with 12LVA24 engines, and 13 had been delivered from CAFL. 68010 has just arrived at Paris Gare St Lazare on an early morning express from Caen. At the time 5 locomotives worked on the Eastern Region of the SNCF, based at Chalindrey, with 8 on the Western Region based at Caen.

Nigerian Railways AEI-Sulzer 1400 hp Co-Co locomotive No 1401

With overseas contracts running in Australia, Malawi, Mozambique and Nigeria, I went on a tour of our African customers in late 1965, also visiting Zimbabwe (then Rhodesia) and South Africa. 29 1400hp Co-Co locomotives for the 3ft 6in gauge lines of the Nigerian Railway Corporation had been ordered from AEI, and the mechanical parts builder was Metropolitan Cammell in Birmingham. They were named after stations of the Nigerian Railways. Here, the first, no 1401 "Lagos" is seen on a train passing through Niger delta country. These locomotives had Vickers-built Sulzer 6LDA28C engines delivering 1400hp at 800rpm and were identical to engines being supplied to the former Commonwealth Railways in Australia for the Port Augusta - Alice Springs 3ft 6in gauge line, subsequently converted to standard gauge.

Class 25 D5240 in Cricklewood Sidings

Back home, things were happening fast, and Sulzer service engineers were commissioning engines at Brush, Loughborough (class 47), Crewe (class 47), Darlington and Derby (class 25). In addition we had "guarantee" engineers in most Regional Diesel Depots. Our service engineers were both British and Swiss, and at the time I took over they numbered 25. Our sub-contractors, Vickers at Barrow-in-Furness, were turning out one Sulzer engine each working day! This photograph of Derby-built D5240 was taken at Cricklewood soon after commissioning in January 1964, and is one of the later "cleaned up" locomotives in the two-tone green livery of the time.

Two 4VEP units on a semi-fast service passing Surbiton
The 4VEPs, following the Bournemouth batch, soon became the standard replacements for the earlier 2BIL, 2HAL and 4LAV stock, being introduced on the Brighton, Portsmouth and other lines. Here two of the later units with 7781 leading, in the original all-blue livery with the polished aluminium BR totem below the driver's cab windows, pass Surbiton on a Bournemouth semi-fast service in September 1967. Note the newly relaid and reballasted crossover at the London end of the down slow platform.

Opposite page, top: **Class 47 on up Bournemouth train entering Surbiton.**
Planning for the Bournemouth electrification, in which I had some involvement, had commenced before I left BR in 1964. In the last stages before electrification, some class 47s were 'borrowed' from the Western Region to enable steam depots to be run down. Rather dirty D1922 (new in January that year and allocated to Ebbw Junction) passes Surbiton with an up Weymouth train in July 1966. It is in the same location as 10202 on page 31, taken some 13 years earlier. Note the miscellaneous collection of BR and ex-Southern coaches, two still sporting the BR two-tone carmine/cream livery, flat bottom rail on all running lines and the dirty two-tone green livery of the locomotive.

Opposite page, lower: **4VEP unit 7701 passing Worting Junction in 1985.**
For "intermediate" services on the Bournemouth line the original proposal had been to build more 2HAP units. As many of these would run in pairs it was therefore cheaper and more practical to build 4-car units. A single 4-motor motor coach and three trailers had proved economical for the Northampton lines so a similar arrangement was used for the Bournemouth line, but with through gangways. Twenty units, classified 4VEP and numbered 7701-20, were built, the first, 7701, still allocated to Bournemouth 17 years later, is passing Worting Junction on 1st October 1980 on a Bournemouth stopping service.

*Left: **Nigerian Railways Train from Kano to Zaria with Co-Co Locomotive 1413***

In 1970, I accompanied two AEI engineers on a "fact finding" visit, the main objective being to study the state of the locomotives prior to the negotiation of a maintenance contract, which would embrace the supervision of main works overhauls and training of personnel, as the Biafran War had left the railways short of skilled staff. To assess the condition of the motive power, several trips were made and here No 1413 is about to work a heavy freight train from Kano to Zaria. We travelled on the locomotive; the saloon, the first vehicle in the train, was provided for our use.

Class 33 No 33026 on 14.10 Waterloo-Salisbury train at Battledown
In 1971, the Class 33s took over the Waterloo-Exeter services following the demise of the Western Region "Warship" diesel-hydraulics, their inauguration being on 6th October, almost 20 years after 10202 began regular diesel working between Waterloo and Exeter. The Class 33 monopoly lasted 8Ω years when class 50s took over because it was necessary by then to reduce the overall timings, but there were still occasions when a class 33 had to deputise. 33026 is west of Battledown flyover with the 14.10 Waterloo-Salisbury train on 31st July 1987.

Opposite page, top: ***Mixed formation of EMU and diesel stock passing Winchfield***
The Bournemouth electrification was unique, and with multiple-unit trains as the basis, limiting electrification to Bournemouth posed a problem for through running to Weymouth. This was solved by using 4-car electric 'tractor' units propelling one or two un-motored (trailer) units to Bournemouth, where one or both were detached and worked forward by specially adapted class 33s. With 'up' trains the class 33 propelled to Bournemouth where a 4-car 'tractor' took over to haul the train to Waterloo. 19 class 33s were converted for remote operation and became sub-class 33/1. These could also control, and be controlled, from electric multiple-units. Here one of the class 33/1s is in control and the first unit is a 4TC (an un-motored trailer unit), the remaining eight being two 4VEPs - all under the control of the driver of the class 33/1. The train is the 17.10 from Waterloo and is passing Winchfield in July 1984. It would divide at Basingstoke, the locomotive and 4TC going forward to Yeovil Junction and the two EMU sets to Eastleigh.

Waterloo-Salisbury stopping train passing Winchfield.

After the class 50s took over the Exeter trains in 1980, the Salisbury semi-fasts continued to be worked for a time by class 33s. Usually the stock was one 4TC set with a class 33/1. Here, the 16.10 Waterloo-Salisbury train is seen passing Winchfield on 27th June 1987 hauled by class 33/0 No 33051 with 4TC set 8012. Winchfield substation is behind the rear coach and today a building contractor has taken over the former goods yard

Table on opposite page:

First use of class 33 to Exeter - 6th October 1971.
Train: 1430 Exeter St. Davids to Waterloo. D6540.
Load 285 tons tare, 305 tons gross.
Heating oad 100 amps = 75Kw = 90 hp approx. Horsepower at rail = 1160 approx.
All speeds from locomotive speedometer. (Train continued to Waterloo due 1816.)

An Engineer on the Southern Diesels and Electrics

Distance Miles	Point	Schedule arr.	Actual arr.	Schedule dep.	Actual dep.	Speed	Notes
	Exeter St. Davids		14.30	14.30			
	Exeter Central	14.33$^{1}/_{2}$	14.33	14.35	14.34$^{1}/_{2}$		
1.05	Exmouth Junction	14.38 pass	14.37$^{1}/_{2}$ pass			38/52	
2.80	Pinhoe Crossing	14.40$^{1}/_{2}$ pass	14.40 pass			30	
8.40	Whimple					60/55	
12.15	Feniton					60/76	
16.75	**Honiton**	14.56	14.55	14.57	14.58$^{3}/_{4}$		
7.00	Seaton Junction					80/71/80	
10.15	**Axminster**	15.08	15.09$^{3}/_{4}$	15.09	15.11		
5.10	Chard	15.17 pass.	15.17$^{1}/_{2}$			64/67	
11.30	Hewish					62	
13.20	Crewkerne					69/80	
21.95	**Yeovil Junction**	15.32	15.28	15.34	15.35$^{1}/_{4}$		
4.60	**Sherbourne**	15.43	15.43$^{1}/_{4}$	15.44	15.46	67	max.
6.10	Templecombe	15.53 pass.	15.55 pass			78/84/64	
13.00	**Gillingham**	15.59	16.01	16.00	16.02		Sigs.
4.10	Semley					49/73	
9.00	Tisbury	16.12$^{1}/_{2}$	16.14$^{1}/_{4}$	16.14	16.15		
4.25	Dinton					78/82	
10.05	Wilton South					34/47	40 res.
12.55	**Salisbury**	16.33$^{1}/_{2}$	16.31	16.36	16.35		
1.10	Tunnel Junction	16.39$^{1}/_{2}$ pass.	16.38$^{1}/_{2}$			43	
5.75	Porton					60	
10.65	Grateley					70/82	
17.45	**Andover Junction**	16.58$^{1}/_{2}$	16.57$^{1}/_{2}$	17.00	17.02$^{3}/_{4}$		
5.08	Hurstbourne					68	
7.11	Whitchurch					72	
10.75	Overton					73	
13.95	Oakley					70	Sigs. To 35
16.05	Worting Junction	17.19$^{1}/_{2}$ pass.	17.19$^{1}/_{4}$			53	
18.55	**Basingstoke**	17.22	17.22$^{3}/_{4}$	17.24	17.24		
5.60	Hook					78	
7.90	Winchfield					81	
11.30	Fleet					82	
14.55	Farnborough					83	
16.80	MP 31		17.38$^{1}/_{2}$			77	eased
19.80	Brookwood				77		
23.50	**Woking**	17.48$^{1}/_{2}$	17.44$^{4}/_{4}$				

Permanent way materials train near Winchfield.

Duties covered by the class 33s embraced all classes of traffic, and the class 33/1s were by no means confined to push-pull trains. Here, in September 1982, 33105 is at Potbridge, west of Winchfield cutting, on a Woking-Eastleigh "permanent way" departmental train consisting of low-sided wagons containing used ballast.

33106 on heavy Newcastle-Poole train passing Battledown

Another shot of a class 33/1, this time 33106, deputising for a class 47 on the Reading-Poole leg of a heavy Newcastle-Poole train in March 1981. The place is Battledown, three miles west of Basingstoke, where the Bournemouth/Weymouth and West of England lines part company. The bridge in the background is the flyover, that carries the up Bournemouth/Weymouth line over the West of England lines.

An Engineer on the Southern Diesels and Electrics

One of the first batch of class 47s - 1507 at Kings Cross
The first order for class 47s was for 20 locomotives, originally numbered D1500-19. Turned out in 1962/3 in two-tone green livery the first batch was allocated to the Eastern Region at Finsbury Park. They were built with both train-heating boilers and electric train heating on a dc system similar to the class 33s, but only vacuum brakes! After initial tests on the LM Region they were allocated to the Eastern Region where the electric heating could not be used as there were then no electrically-heated coaches on the Eastern Region! Here 1507, painted in all-over blue livery backs on to a train for Hull at Kings Cross on a dull Saturday afternoon in September 1968.

Opposite page: **'Kestrel' entering Kings Cross on a train from Newcastle**
In the 1960s, there were a number of private ventures with the next generation of motive power in mind. In building "Kestrel", a private venture by Hawker-Siddeley and Brush, there was much more than just British Railways in mind. At the time, this was the only 4000hp locomotive in the world with a single engine. Completed in 1967, and formally handed over to British Railways for trial and evaluation on 19th January 1968, "Kestrel" weighed 126 tons, and was designed for a top speed of 110 mph. It emerged at the time of serious permanent way damage on the LM Region, and it was not permitted initially on fast passenger trains. To permit running at 100 mph, class 47 bogies and traction motors were substituted. Power was provided by a Sulzer 16LVA24 diesel engine rated at 4000hp at 1100rpm. "Kestrel" could not be usefully employed on British Railways, and was eventually sold to Russia in 1971. Here on class 47 bogies, "Kestrel" is emerging from Kings Cross Tunnel on a train from Newcastle on the same dull Saturday as the previous picture in September 1968.

Class 47 on Ripple Lane - Fawley tank car train passing Battledown
Except for a short time in 1967, the Southern Region had no class 47 allocation but many worked through trains to places such as Southampton, Poole, Brighton and Dover. A regular working was on Fawley refinery oil tank trains. 47085 "Mammoth" is on the Ripple Lane-Eastleigh empty tank cars in March 1987, approaching Battledown Flyover. This was before sectorisation with its various liveries, 47085 then being painted plain 'rail' blue.

Opposite page, top: **RCTS "V.S.O.E" Pullman train with two electro-diesels at Romsey.**
On 16th April 1983, the Railway Correspondence and Travel Society organised a railtour for its members using the British Venice Simplon Orient Express Pullmans. The tour ran from Victoria via Horsham to Chichester, Fareham and Eastleigh to Romsey. After a break, the tour returned to London Victoria via the Laverstock curve, Andover, Worting Junction, Woking, Staines, Clapham Junction, and Olympia to bring the stock the right way round for the next charter. Two class 73/1 electro-diesels were provided as the section from Farlington Junction to Fareham was not then electrified. 73142 "Broadlands" and 73129 "City of Winchester" are standing at Romsey. Unhappily, an overspeed trip rendered diesel power unobtainable from one locomotive for most of the non-electrified section so progress was rather pedestrian! Electric power made up time between Worting Junction and Woking with 90+ mph for most of the way and 100 mph just before Pirbright Junction.

Opposite page, lower: **Sulzer in USA. Four Southern Pacific prototypes at Eugene, Oregon 1980**
In the late 1970s/early 1980s Sulzer made a brief foray back into rail traction with engines designed primarily for stationary power generation and ships' auxiliaries, that could also be accommodated in locomotives. Many of these engines were built by licensees and in the late 1970s a licensee was being negotiated in the USA (later taken up by Waukesha - a Dresser Industries Company). Some American railroads were seeking alternatives to General Motors, so re-manufacturer Morrison-Knudsen of Boise Idaho came up with a proposal to re-engine some obsolescent locomotives as demonstrators. Four GE U25Bs of Southern Pacific were fitted with Swiss-built Sulzer 12ASV25/30 engines, developing 3200hp (2,800 hp traction). The four locomotives are waiting at Eugene, Oregon for a train to Roseburg on 16 May 1980, on which I accompanied two senior BR engineers. Later in the same year, six 16-cylinder engines of 4000hp were fitted to rebuilt EMD SD45s of Burlington Northern RR and 4 more to SD45s of Union Pacific RR. All have now been taken out of service.

Hybrid 3-car diesel-electric multiple unit 1401 at Worting Junction.
The last 2-car diesel-electric units to be made up to 3-cars were the four used on the Hastings-Ashford and the Bexhill West services. Some driving trailers became spare on withdrawal of the hybrid 3-car units known as the "Tadpoles", and four were transferred to units 1119-22, which were renumbered 1401-4. 1401 is working a Basingstoke-Salisbury stopping train past Worting Junction in March 1985. Note the redundant driving cab at the Basingstoke end of the centre car and the two first class compartments in the rear car. These four units have now been withdrawn.

Opposite page, top: ***Liverpool-Poole train entering Basingstoke.***
Before the introduction of HST sets, most Inter-Regional workings were in the hands of class 47/4s. Here 47521 enters Basingstoke off the Reading line with the 08.55 Liverpool Lime Street-Poole train on Sunday 26th September 1987. Note the miscellaneous collection of liveries - three are here represented on the air-conditioned Mk2 coaches. The then panel signal box is behind the train. 47521 will have taken over the train at Reading.

Opposite page, lower: ***"Farewell St Leonards' Staff" special to Weymouth with unit 203001.***
On 12 September 1987, a special was run from St Leonards to Weymouth Quay and back, on which I was a guest, to celebrate the depot's 30 years of working with the Hastings diesel-electrics, just replaced by electrification. The depot was closed and has now been sold. The special train was provided by four long "Hastings" vehicles formed into unit 203001, used for a time between Hastings and Ashford. The rear motor coach had recently been named "Hastings". Seen here entering Southampton, the 30 mph speed restriction sign seems to have been positioned for the occasion.

73122 with Poole-Northfleet cement empties at Worting Junction

The Bournemouth electrification required another 43 electro-diesels, and as BR workshops were fully committed, the order went to English Electric's Vulcan Works at Newton-le-Willows near Warrington. Building commenced in 1965, and some important changes were made from the prototypes. Except for the spring rates, the bogies were identical to those under the power cars of the 4REP units and the traction motors were interchangeable, although in this instance they were pressure ventilated. Numbered E6007-49, the control system was modified to use one control jumper. Maximum speed was increased to 90 mph. Although intended primarily for freight, the class 73s have provided stop-gaps on two occasions on Bournemouth passenger services. First just prior to and just after electrification to 'fill-in' for delayed EMU stock, and again when they replaced 4REPs withdrawn for their traction equipment to be transferred to the new "Wessex" EMUs. 73122 (later 73207) "County of East Sussex", in Inter City livery, takes the Poole-Northfleet cement empties past Worting Junction in February 1985.

Bournemouth-Waterloo semi-fast approaching Battledown with 73122

73122, operating as an express passenger locomotive, hauls the 14.00 Bournemouth to Waterloo on 31st July 1987, climbing the 1 in 106 southern ramp to the Battledown flyover in the interim period between 4REP and 5WES, when the traction equipment was being revamped for fitting to the new stock for the Bournemouth-Weymouth extension. Here, the stock is 2x4TC sets, the first having been re-formed to 4RTC and renumbered 2803, a restaurant car from a 4REP having been substituted for the former open second. Heavier trains needed two class 73s to maintain the fast schedules.

Mixed formation train with EMUs and electro-diesel locomotive
Another possibility was the mixing of EMU and 4TC sets as seen here on 11th July 1987, the reason for the formation being unknown to me. The train was a semi-fast service from Waterloo to Bournemouth with a 4VEP, class 423, 7750 (later 3050) leading a 4TC/4RTC formation past Winchfield with 73126 (later named "Kent & East Sussex Railway") at the rear. There were once goods yards on both sides of the line.

Opposite page, top: **73125 propelling Waterloo-Bournemouth train near Battledown**
An earlier shot taken near Worting Junction on 19th March 1987. The locomotive propelling was 73125 (later 73204 "Stewarts Lane 1860-1985") with the same train formation with 4TC 8015 leading 4RTC 2805. The train was the 13.44 from Waterloo to Bournemouth. The schedules of the semi-fasts had been lengthened slightly, so that timekeeping was possible with either locomotive and 8TC or "Greyhound" 4CEP/BEP formations.

Opposite page, lower: **'Sandite' unit 1067 formed from 'Hastings' DEMU stock at Betchworth**
New stock from old! An ever-present problem is that of loss of adhesion in the Autumn caused by both leaf-mulch and the damp, slippery film left on rails, a problem always treated with derision by the ever critical media. In earlier years, trees were not allowed to grow in cuttings to alleviate these problems, but today the environmentalists complain if they are removed. In latter years specially equipped trains have been provided to both scrub and clean the rails. Here "Sandite" 4-car unit 1067, converted from ex-Hastings "long" vehicles leaves Betchworth on the Guildford-Redhill line on 30th October 1992. The special vehicle containing the scrubbing and conditioning equipment is on the level crossing, in the shadow of the former station house.

Class 33/2 in its final form. 33201 at Tonbridge on a PW train

I was "Project Engineer" for these locomotives and retain a "proprietorial" interest, still thinking of them as "my" locomotives! Time has also taken toll of the class 33s although they have outlived all of the other 'Modernisation' Bo-Bo type 2s of the late '50s and early '60s. Here class 33/2 33201, formerly D6586, built in February 1962, the first of the "Slim Jims", passes Tonbridge on a permanent way engineer's train on 1st June 1993. 33201 is in the civil engineer's so-called "Dutch" livery, and at the time of the photograph still retained its electric train heating equipment in working order.